CW00553649

LET US BE MERRY

British Library Cataloguing-in-publication data
A catalogue record for this book is available from the British
Library.
ISBN 0 9526031 1 X

Copyright this selection © 1996 by Roy Palmer and Gwilym
Davies

First published in 1996 by Green Branch Press, Kencot Lodge,
Kencot, Lechlade, Gloucestershire GL7 3QX, United Kingdom.
Tel. 01367 860588. Fax 01367 860619.

All rights reserved. No part of this work may be reproduced or
stored in an information retrieval system, other than short extracts
for the purposes of review, without the express permission of the
publisher.

Roy Palmer and Gwilym Davies have asserted their right under
the Copyright, Designs and Patents Act 1988 to be identified as
authors of this work.

Typeset by Green Branch Press.

Printed and bound by Litho Impressions, Unit H1, New Yatt
Business Centre, New Yatt, Witney, Oxon OX8 6NN.

Cover picture: "The Country Carol Seller"(1869). by "Cuthbert
Bede" (Rev. Edward Bradley).

Let Us Be Merry

TRADITIONAL CHRISTMAS SONGS AND CAROLS FROM GLOUCESTERSHIRE

Edited by
Gwilym Davies and Roy Palmer

Green Branch

Contents

Introduction

The constant barrage of Christmas music which can now be heard from October onwards leads many to believe that there are only a handful of carols in existence. By the same token, local repertoires or regional variations in tunes or texts are ignored. In fact, the carols that we hear in every concert, radio programme or supermarket loudspeaker, worthy though they may be, are only a handful of those that are available.

Singing at Christmas is probably as old as Christmas itself. At least one carol in English has survived from the thirteenth century, and many from subsequent periods. The Reformation put a halt to the singing of carols in churches for a number of years, and even as late as the 1780s, there was only one, 'While Shepherds Watched', that was accepted in Anglican services.

The Victorians produced many new carols, and established them in the church. Some of these, such as 'Hark the Herald' and 'We Three Kings' remain favourites today. They may well be over familiar and are frequently parodied.

Running in parallel with the church tradition were traditional carols handed down within families or local communities, with variations of words and music. One such was 'The Holly and the 'Ivy' , now universally known thanks to a Gloucestershire woman, Mary Ann Clayton, a chimney sweep from Chipping Campden, whose version Cecil Sharp noted in 1908 and subsequently published:

The holly and the ivy, now they are both full grown,
Of all the trees that are in the wood, the holly bears the crown.

One might be forgiven for thinking that this version is the only one in existence, but this is far from the case; many other variants of this fine carol exist, one of which is published in this volume (page 44).

Not all traditional carols deal with the familiar themes of shepherds, angels and the infant Jesus. Some, still considered as carols by those who sang them, can be stern and even vengeful, with a strong emphasis on both morality and mortality. A couplet in 'Christmas is now drawing near at hand' (page 42) reminds us:

Remember, man, that thou wast made of clay
And in this world thou hast not long to stay.

There is no hint of comfort in those words.

Other carols, such as 'The Bitter Willow' (page 36) and 'The Cherry Tree Carol' (page 32) draw less on the authentic than on the apocryphal gospels, with their rather more violent attitudes.

Such carols were often treasured and passed on down the generations by word of mouth. The printed word aided this process - at least with the words, as tunes were not included. Single carol sheets, known as broadsides, and booklets, known as garlands, were hawked at markets, fairs, in the streets and even from door to door.

One such garland, entitled *A Choice Collection of Christmas Carols, No. 1*, was printed in the latter half of the eighteenth century by Samuel Harward, who worked at Tewkesbury, and had additional shops in Cheltenham and Gloucester. The collection of five carols includes 'Have you not heard of our Saviour's love', 'A virgin most pure as the prophets do tell' and 'On Christmas day all Christians sing', versions all of which have circulated in Gloucestershire's living tradition in recent years (see pages 31, 24 and 14 of this book.). It is not known whether Harward issued further carols.

It was attitudes within communities, particularly within families, which determined whether carols survived or not. The related Bishop and Hill families of Bromsberrow Heath in the north-west of Gloucestershire preserved many carols. Thomas Bishop was a well-sinker and water diviner, but when work was slack and Christmas approached, he and his neighbours would turn out with their morris dances to tour the big houses of the area. They would be invited in for refreshments, after which they would sing some carols. Thomas's daughter, Emily, born in 1881, learned many pieces from him such as 'Christmas is now drawing near at hand' (page 42), 'Divers and Lazarus' (page 40) and 'On Christmas Night' (page 14). Emily's sister Beatrice married into the Hill family, members of which still live in Bromsberrow Heath, and two carols are included from the late Ivor Hill (pages 12 and 44).

The Partridge family from Cinderford have likewise contributed. John Partridge (1885-1961), a Cinderford miner, sang 'The Cherry Tree Carol' (page 32) and 'Shepherds of Old' (page 26). His son, Stan, followed him into mining. With his wife and family, straight after midnight on Christmas Eve, he sings 'With Joy Awake' (page 11), which comes from his Methodist background.

Songs have also been provided by members of the gypsy community, namely the Smiths from the Cheltenham/Tewkesbury area, and the Brazil (pronounced 'brazzle') family from Gloucester. Lementina ('Lemmie') Brazil was in her eighties in 1966 when she recorded 'The Bitter Willow' (page 36), whilst her brother Danny, now aged 85, remembers the old songs with fierce affection.

The West Gallery singers of Anglican churches, of whom Thomas Hardy painted an affectionate portrait in *Under the Greenwood Tree*, have also contributed to the tradition. 'Hark! hark! what news the angels bring' (page 20) may well derive from such a source.

One must not forget children's carol singing, a tradition which persists to this day with varying degrees of skill and commitment. In *Cider with Rosie*, Laurie Lee provides a classic account. A performance might end with a shout through the keyhole of:

Knock on the knocker! Ring at the bell!
Give us a penny for singing so well!

Similar chants can be found in this book, such as 'The Cock flew up in the yew tree' (page 64) and 'We wish you a merry Christmas' (page 68).

Most of the carols here are found in different forms in other parts of the country, and Gloucestershire cannot lay exclusive claim to them. Moreover, attaching regional labels can be misleading. The so-called 'Sussex Carol' has appeared in various parts of England, including Gloucestershire, as 'On Christmas Night' (page 14). There is one carol, however, which is as Gloucestershire as limestone walls, Old Spot pigs, cider, cheese and elvers, namely the renowned 'Gloucestershire Wassail'. Even in recent memory, this was beloved of folk in the south of the county as a song and a custom, with variations from village to village.

Gloucestershire is a county from which a large number of carols have been collected. This is particularly so when one reaches the north-western side of the county, the area bordering on Herefordshire and Worcestershire, counties equally rich in the carolling tradition. Much of this has been recorded in recent years, thus providing fresh versions of old carols and shedding new light on the tradition.

Rich though Gloucestershire is in Christmas carols and seasonal songs of the turn of the year, there has been no book which included a representative selection. Some scattered examples have been published, but much is inaccessible, hidden in manuscript collections or held in private recordings. This work sets out to preserve some of these carols and songs as they were, and are, sung in Gloucestershire. It is hoped that they will be taken up by choirs, schools, local organisations, folk clubs, and indeed by anyone interested in a time-honoured tradition.

Two items of recent composition by Gloucestershire people have been included, 'The Christmas Lament' (page 54) and 'The Lambskin Carol' (page 52). We hope that these will stimulate new writing along old lines and a prolongation of the tradition which will ensure in turn that as well as a past the people's carol will have a future.

Acknowledgements

The editors and publisher would like to thank for their songs, all the singers, past and present, who have contributed to this book;

for invaluable financial support, Cheltenham and Gloucestershire Rural Initiative Fund, Gloucestershire Folk, and the National Folk Music Fund;

for advice and assistance, Paul Burgess, Rev. Richard Hart, Leslie Shepard, Grenville Sheringham, Malcolm Taylor (Vaughan Williams Memorial Library, Cecil Sharp House), Ursula Vaughan Williams, and Dr Robin Wiltshire (Centre for English Cultural Traditions, University of Sheffield - Russell Wortley Collection);

for communicating songs, and giving permission for them to be reproduced, Richard Chidlaw ('The Christmas Lament'), the Percy Grainger Society ('The Lilywhite Boys'), Peter Kennedy ('The Cherry Tree Carol', 'On Christmas Night'), the Library of Congress ('Sherborne Mummers' Song' from the Carpenter Collection), Bob Patten and Andrew Taylor ('Brockweir Wassail', Jacob's Well', 'Our Saviour's

Love', 'A Virgin Unspotted', verses 4-7), Peter Shepheard ('As I walked by the Riverside', 'The Bitter Willow', 'Come all you lucky gentlemen'), Maddy Taylor ('The Lambskin Carol'), Diana Wortley ('Christmas is now drawing near at hand', 'Divers and Lazarus'), Mike Yates ('The Holly and the Ivy', 'List' our Merry Carol'), Fred Archer ('Hark! hark! what news the angels bring'); for illustrations, Pat Palmer (pp. 13 and 19), Mrs Thelma Hill (p. 15), the late Mrs M. Williams (p.17), Victoria and Albert Museum (p. 45) and Richard Chidlaw (p. 61)

Tunes of previously unpublished material have been transcribed by Gwilym Davies unless otherwise stated.

With Joy Awake

Sung by Stan and Gwen Partridge, Cinderford; recorded by Pat and Roy Palmer, July 1994. Transcribed by Gordon Ashman and Robert Bunting. Like his father John (singer of 'The Cherry Tree Carol' (page 32), Stan (now aged 80) is an ex-miner. He says of 'With joy awake': 'It is the first carol we do sing after midnight on Christmas Eve'. The editors have not seen it elsewhere.

11

List' our Merry carol

List' our mer-ry car-ol on this bles-sed morn, For our lov-ing sa-viour on Christ-mas Day was born. There so peace-ful, sleep-ing, like a flower he lay, Christ, our lov-ing sa-viour, born on Christ-mas Day. Christ, our lov-ing sa-viour, born on Christ-mas Day.

Chorus

Ca-rol, ca-rol gai-ly, ca-rol on our way, Christ, our lov-ing sa-viour, born on Christ-mas Day. Christ, our lov-ing sa-viour, born on Christ-mas Day.

See the star is beaming in the radiant east,
And our song of glory never more shall cease.
Banish all unkindness, be of gentle will;
Angels ever near us carol to us still,
Angels ever near us carol to us still.

Joyful, joyful tidings break upon the earth,
Sing the saviour's glory, tell his wondrous worth.
Every hill and valley, clad in pure white snow,
Breathes a merry carol, echo sweet and low.
Breathes a merry carol, echo sweet and low.

The singer here, Ivor Hill of Bromsberrow Heath, was recorded by Gwilym Davies and Mike Yates in 1980 and can be heard on the cassette, *The Horkey Load*, vol. 2 (see Discography). The carol was published in *Hart's Choruses, Anthems, Etc.* (c.1903). The Hills are related to the Bishops from whom several carols in this volume were noted. Tune transcribed by Pat Palmer.

Bromsberrow Church. Emily Bishop is buried here
Photo: Pat Palmer

On Christmas Night

On Christ - mas night all Christ - ians sing, To hear what news the an - gels bring, News of great joy, cause of great mirth, News of our great re - dee - mer's birth.

The king of angels and of men,
The king of kings of earth and heaven;
Angels and men with joy may sing
To hear and bless the new-born king.

Angels and men sing in the air
For none their ruin can repair,
And prisoners in their chains rejoice
To hear the echo of their voice.

And now on earth shall men be sad,
Our saviour comes to make us glad;
From sin and ill to set us free
And buy for us our liberty.

And now from darkness we have light,
Which makes all angels sing this night.
'Glory to God and peace to men
Now and for ever more, amen'.

14

Sung by Emily Bishop of Bromsberrow Heath, recorded by Peter Kennedy, 1952, and issued on the cassette *No, Sir, No* (see Discography). Emily Bishop (1879-1961) learned songs and carols from her father, Thomas, well-sinker, water diviner and morris dancer. 'On Christmas Night', despite having been dubbed 'The Sussex Carol' by the composer, Ralph Vaughan Williams, was once known all over England. Cecil Sharp noted a version from William Bayliss of Buckland, Gloucestershire in 1909. It dates from a century before that, since it was one of Bishop Luke Wadding's *Smale Garland of Pious and Godly Songs*, published at Ghent in 1684. The printer, Samuel Harward of Tewkesbury, issued another in *A Choice Collection of Christmas Carols, No.1*, which appeared in the late eighteenth century. Harward's third verse has the more cheerful 'That Christ man's ruin will repair', and he gives an additional, penultimate stanza:

> Now sin depart, behold his grace;
> And death, his life comes in thy place;
> And now thou may'st thy terror see;
> And power great must conquer'd be.

Emily Bishop
Photo: courtesy of Mrs Thelma Hill

Jacob's Well

This had she known, her drooping mind
For richer draught had sighed;
Nor had Messiah ever kind
That richer draught denied.

This ancient well no glass so true
Britannia's image shows;
Now Jesus travels Britain through,
But who the stranger knows?

But Britain must this stranger know
Or soon our loss deplore.
Behold the living waters flow.
Come drink and thirst no more.
Behold the living waters flow.
Come drink and thirst no more.

Jacob's Well was in the Samarian city of Sychar (called Shekem in the Old Testament). The encounter there between Christ and the woman of Samaria is described in *John*, chapter 4. The curious carol on the subject is extremely rare. No version from oral tradition is on record at Cecil Sharp House, and the editors have seen a text only in *A Good Christmas Box*, published in Dudley in 1847. Our version, from Charley Williams (1909-1983), a native of Brockweir, was recorded by Bob Patten and Andrew Taylor at Bream in November 1977 and is used with permission. Tune transcribed by Pat Palmer.

Charley Williams (1909-1983)
Photographed in 1971 (picture courtesy of Mrs M Williams)

O grand and O bright

'I bring you', said he, 'from a glorious dream
A message both gladsome and bold [good]:
A saviour has come to this world unknown,
And he lies in a manger of wood'.

The shepherds amazed, the little lambs gazed,
As the darkness was turned into light;
No voice was then heard of his wonderful word,
Of his wonderful conquest was won.
[No voice then was heard from man, beast nor bird,
So sudden and solemn the sight.]

Then goodwill to men, our life's but a span
Our souls are so sinful and bright [vile];
So pray, Christians, pray, and let Christmas Day
Have a tear as well as a smile.

Mrs Betty Aldridge of Cam sang this to Pat and Roy Palmer in January 1995. She learned it from her late husband, Ray Lord, who prized it so much that she had the opening words inscribed on his tombstone at Frampton-on-Severn. It can be traced back to George Lord, who was born in Gloucestershire's Cambridge in 1861, though how he acquired the carol remains unclear. The text was published in the mid-nineteenth century by a Birmingham ballad printer under the title of 'The Worcestershire Carol'. Versions have been reported from 1920s carol singers in the Epney-Longney-Morton Valence area, from around about Worcester in the 1930s and from Castle Frome, Herefordshire in 1978. Even so, the carol is now very rare. Tune transcribed by Pat Palmer.

Betty Aldridge, January 1995
Photo: Pat Palmer

Hark! hark! what news the angels bring

There was a day, a blessed morn
The saviour of mankind was born;
Born of a maiden, a virgin pure,
Born without sin, without sin, from guilt, from guilt secure.

Hail! blessed Mary, full of grace,
Blessed above, blessed above all mortal race
Whose sacred womb brought forth in one
A God, a sav', a God, a saviour, saviour and a son.

Hail! mighty prince! eternal king!
Let heaven and earth, let heaven and earth rejoice and sing,
Angels and men with one accord,
Break forth in songs, break forth in songs to praise, to praise the Lord.

Now from great darkness we have light
Which made all angels, made all angels sing this night.
Glory to God and peace to men
Now and for ever, now and for evermore, evermore, amen.

This is one of several carols from Ashton-under-Hill, now in Worcestershire, but until 1930 in Gloucestershire. The carols used to be sung there on Christmas Day and on Old Christmas Day (5 January) and were noted, arranged and published by Amy Roberson, the organist of St Barnabas Church at Ashton-under-Hill. The carols were sung in the village up to the early 1950's. The carol is certainly old and can be traced back to at least the early 18th century. It probably belonged to the West Gallery tradition; a version is still sung in South Yorkshire pubs where it is known as 'The old hark, hark.' Its last verse is shared with 'On Christmas Night' (page 14).

Mr Fred Archer, who kindly communicated the Ashton carols to the editors, writes in *The Distant Scene* (1967), describing Boxing Day in Ashton:

'The bell ringers had arrived and we were not in bed. 'Shall we sing you a couple of carols, Mam?' Mother said 'Certainly, Walt. Having a good Christmas?' Walt said, 'Oi, but I ca'unt sing like I used to years agu'. By the light of Walt's stable lantern hung on a forked stick, the five ringers started. Job Wheatcroft on crutches (he'd lost a leg at Mons) gave the note. He had a deep bass voice. They sang *All hail and praise the Sacred Morn*, then *Arise, ye sleepy souls arise*. These two pieces were local carols, and until a few years before, they had sung another local one, the Withy carol. Lastly, the *pièce de résistance* came - *While Shepherds Watched*, to the tune Lyneham. I have never heard carol singing like it; it was so sincere. It could have been the first Christmas.'

The Seven Joys of Mary

The first good joy that Mary had, it was the joy of one, To
work on earth be-gun, good man, and hap-py may we be. Praise

see her own son, Jesus Christ, his work on earth be-gun; His
Father, Son and Ho-ly Ghost through all e-ter-ni- ty.

The next good joy that Mary had, it was the joy of two,
To see her own son, Jesus Christ, making the lame to go.
Making the lame to go, good man, and happy may we be;
Praise Father, Son and Holy Ghost through all eternity.

(And so on, with)

three........making the blind to see
four.........preaching the scriptures o'er
five..........making the dead alive
six............upon the crucifix
seven......ascending into heaven.

The enumeration in song of Mary's joys goes back perhaps to the fourteenth century with the 'Joyes Fyve' of the Sloane manuscripts. The catalogue sometimes extends to twelve, as in the example noted by Cecil Sharp in 1907 from Joseph Evans of Old Sodbury. Dick Parsons, (recorded in 1979 in Cheltenham by Gwilym Davies) sticks to seven in the version he learned some 70 years earlier at Shurdington, on the outskirts of Cheltenham. This version can be heard on the cassette *All brought up on Cider* (see Discography).

Rev J.E.Vaux writes in his book, *Church Folklore* (1894): 'It was formerly the custom in the north of England for poor women to carry about during Advent a couple of dolls dressed, the one to represent the Saviour and the other the Virgin Mary. A halfpenny was expected from every person to whom they were exhibited. It was esteemed a sign of very bad luck to any household that had not been visited by the "Advent Images" before Christmas Eve at the latest. The bearers of the images sung the well-known carol, beginning "The first good joy that Mary had."'"

The writer, William E. Adams, who was born in 1832 in Cheltenham, described local customs in *Memoirs of a Social Atom* (1903). He reports that the carol was sung by children, who ended their performance with these words:

God bless the master of this house
Likewise the mistress too,
And all the little children
Who about the house do go,
With money in their pockets
And silver in their purse.
Please, ma'am to give us a halfpenny
And you'll be none the worse.
H-o-o-p!

A Virgin Unspotted

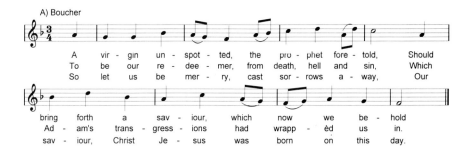

A) Boucher

A vir - gin un - spot - ted, the pro - phet fore - told, Should
To be our re - dee - mer, from death, hell and sin, Which
So let us be mer - ry, cast sor - rows a - way, Our

bring forth a sav - iour, which now we be - hold
Ad - am's trans - gress - ions had wrapp - èd us in.
sav - iour, Christ Je - sus was born on this day.

B) Williams

Now Mar - y's full time be - ing come as we find, She brought forth her

first born to save all man - kind. The inn be - ing so full for this

hea - ven - ly guest, No room was there found for to lay him to

Chorus:
rest. So let us be mer - ry, cast sor - rows a - way; Our

sa - viour, Christ Jes - us, was born on this day.

In Bethlehem city, in Jewry it was
That Joseph and Mary together did pass,
For to be taxèd, like many a one more:
Great Caesar commanded the same should be so.

Then God sent an angel from heaven so high
To certain poor shepherds in fields as they lie,
To tell them no longer in sorrow to stay
Because our saviour was so born today.

Now Mary's full time being come as we find,
She brought forth her first born to save all mankind.
The inn being so full for this heavenly guest,
No room was there found for to lay him to rest.

Then Mary, oh Mary, so meek and so mild,
Soon wrapped up in swaddling this heavenly child;
Contented she laid him where oxen do feed.
The great God of mercy approved of this deed.

To teach us humility all this was done,
And learn us from henceforth sheer pride for to shun.
A manger his cradle though he came from above,
The great God of mercy, of peace and of love.

Then presently after, the shepherds did spy
That numbers of angels to stand in the sky;
All merrily talking, so sweetly did sing,
All glory and praise to our heavenly king.

At least one schoolboy caroller called this 'The Virgin and Spotty'. A pity, because it is a venerable piece, of which the text (though probably dating from the previous century) was first printed in 1661, and the tune (which proved to be one of many) in 1741. Samuel Harward published a set of words at Tewkesbury in the late eighteenth century, and in the same town, Cecil Sharp took down a tune in 1908 from Mrs Elizabeth Smitherd ('Smilhard' according to census records), aged 65. Our first tune and verses 1-3 come from Harold Boucher (1907-1992) of Churchdown, aged 81 when Gwilym Davies recorded him, who learned them as a boy carol singer at Staunton, near Newent. Mr Boucher's memory failed him at the point where by coincidence another singer's recollection began; that of Mr Charley Williams of Brockweir (see note to 'Jacob's Well').

Shepherds of Old

As the shep - herds of old their flocks were a-
tend - ing, To guard them from harm and from dan - ger by
night, They saw a bright an - gel from hea - ven des-
cend - ing which filled them with fear and a - larm at the sight.

But the angel said: 'Fear not, glad tidings I'll bring you,
Not wholly to you but to all upon earth,
For this day in Bethlehem city a saviour is born you.
Be glad that ye shepherds rejoice in the birth'.

As soon as the shepherds had heard these glad tidings
A host of immortals appeared unto them.
So sweetly they were singing: 'To God be all glory.
Peace be upon earth, and goodwill to all men.

'Let us unite in our hearts as we raise our glad voices.
Hallelujah to God in the highest of heaven'.

Sung by John Partridge (for whom, see page 11), Cinderford; recorded by Seamus Ennis in September, 1953. Verse 2 was sung to music AA, 2 to BB, and 4 to A. The editors have not seen this carol elsewhere. Tune transcribed by Pat Palmer.

While Shepherds Watched

A) Stevens family

While shep- herds watched their flocks by night, all seat - ed on ground (all seat- ed on the ground), the an - gel of the Lord came down and glo- ry shone a- round and glo- ry shone a - round and glo - , and glo - ry shone a- round.

B) Jones

While shep - herds watched their flocks by night, all seat - ed on the an - gel of the Lord came down, and glo - ry shone a-

1.
ground, all seat - ed on the ground, The
round, and glo - ry shone a -

2.
round. 'Fear not', said he, for

might - y dread had seized their trou - bled mind. 'Glad tid- ings of great

joy I bring to you and all man - kind' to you and all man - kind.

C) Phelps

While shep- herds watched their flocks by night, all seat - ed on the
not', said he, for might - y dread had seized their trou - bled

ground, The an - gel of the Lord came down, and glo - ry shone a-
mind, 'Glad tid - ings of great joy I bring, to you and all man-

1.
round. 'Fear

2. *Chorus*
kind. Sweet chim- ing Christ - mas bells, sweet

chim- ing Christ - mas bells, They cheer us on our heav'n- ly way, sweet chim - ing

bells, They cheer us on our heav'n - ly way, sweet chim - ing bells.

28

'Fear not', said he, for mighty dread
Had seized their troubled minds,
'Glad tidings of great joy I bring
To you and all mankind.

'To you in David's town this day
Is born of David's line
A saviour who is Christ our Lord
And this shall be the sign.

'The heavenly babe you there shall find
To human view displayed,
All meanly wrapped in swathing bands
And in a manger laid.'

Thus spake the seraph, and forthwith
Appeared a shining throng
Of angels praising God, who thus
Addressed their joyful song.

'All glory be to God on high
And to the earth be peace.
Goodwill henceforth from heaven to men
Begin and never cease.'

Chorus of version C

Sweet chiming Christmas bells
Sweet chiming Christmas bells
They cheer us on our heavenly way,
Sweet chiming bells
They cheer us on our heavenly way
Sweet chiming bells.

'We brought no music, the carols were in our heads. 'Let's give 'em "Wild Shepherds"', said Jack. We began in confusion, plunging into a wreckage of keys, of different words and tempo; but we gathered our strength; he who sang loudest took the rest of us with him, and the carol took shape, if not sweetness'.

Laurie Lee's remarks in *Cider with Rosie* remind us that this was the best known and loved of all the carols. For the best part of a century after the text (possibly written by Nahum Tate) first appeared in 1700 it was the only one which found favour in Anglican services. A wide variety of tunes saw service, now usually narrowed down to one, 'Winchester Old'. However, many communities retained their own traditional airs, and three from Gloucestershire are given here. The first (A., recorded by Gwilym and Carol Davies in 1977) comes from Mrs Madge Stevens (aged 73) of Bisley. Until recently, the Stevens family used to sing it every Christmas in the local pubs of Bisley, together with 'The Waysailing Bowl' (see page 56). The second (B., communicated to Roy Palmer in January 1995) is from Mel Jones of Newent, who heard it sung in 1947 by Bill Evans, a local carpenter, in the Royal Exchange Inn at Hartpury, accompanied by the landlord, Harold Merriman, a player (and maker) of banjos. The third (C., recorded by Gwilym Davies in 1975) was learned by Mrs Muriel Phelps of Cheltenham from her father and uncles, who sang it every Christmas to the accompaniment of concertinas. This version is known today to the Salvation Army. Tunes transcribed by Carol Davies.

Our Saviour's Love

Give to the poor and you lend it to the Lord;
The cheerful giver God will well reward.
[In that sweet place where saints and angels dwell.]
How soon our death may come not tongue can tell.

The sin of drunkenness leave off in time,
For this is a [sad, notorious crime].
Live sober lives [and lay that sin aside,
Nay, likewise the horrid sin of pride].

Known in Herefordshire, Worcestershire and Gloucestershire, this is another carol which circulated on ballad sheets. Monmouth, where one example was printed, is only a few miles from Brockweir where the singer of this version, Charley Williams, was born and brought up. Recorded in 1977 by Bob Patten and Andrew Taylor; used with permission. Tune transcribed by Pat Palmer.

The Cherry Tree Carol

Now Joseph was an old man, and an old man was he, And he married Mary, the Queen of Galilee, And he married Mary, the Queen of Galilee.

Now Joseph and Mary walking down the garden green,
Where cherries hang heavily on every limb.

'Pick me some cherries, Joseph, pick me some cherries, do,
Pick me some cherries, Joseph, that hang on the bough.'

Then up spake old Joseph with his words so unkind,
'Let the man gather the cherries that owneth the child.'

Then up spake our saviour all in his mother's arms [womb]:
'Bow down, thou blessed cherry tree, that Mary may have some.'

The very top branches bowed down to her feet:
'Now you can see, Joseph, there are cherries for me.

'My child shall not be christened in silver nor in gold,
But in some twiggèd cradle where the babes are rocked all.'
                              [That rocks on the mould.]

Then Mary placed her own child upon her knee,
Saying, 'Son, come now and tell us what this world it shall be'.

'The moon it shall be darkened and be burst into blood,
And this world set on fire by the vengeance of God.'

Spoken
We wish you a merry Christmas.

This lengthy ballad, based partly on the apocryphal, partly on the authentic gospels, and probably of medieval origin, has three episodes. The first gives the story of the cherry tree. In the second, an angel announces the baby's imminent birth (see 'As Joseph was a-walking', page 34). Finally, the infant Jesus relates to Mary his vision of the future. 'The Cherry Tree Carol', sung in 1952 by a Cinderford miner, John Partridge (1885-1961), and recorded by Maud Karpeles and Pat Shaw, deals mainly with the first episode, though it has one verse on the second (no. 7) and two on the third (nos. 8 and 9). It can be heard on the cassette, *The Bitter Withy: Early English Folk Carols* (see Discography). Tune transcribed by Richard Chidlaw. This carol was also at one time sung by the Brazil family of Gloucester gypsies.

As Joseph was a-walking

As Jo - seph was a - walk - ing He heard an an - gel sing: 'This
ver - y night shalt thou be born To be our lord and king.
[there shall be born On earth our heavenly king.]

'His birthplace shall be neither
In housen or in hall,
But in a wooden manger rude
Laid in the oxen's stall.

'His clothing shall be neither
In purple or in pall,
But in the linen white and fair
That unseen baby's all.'
[As wear the babies all.]

As Joseph was a-walking
Thus did the angels sing:
'This very night shall Christ be born,
Our glorious lord and king.'

This version of the second part of 'the Cherry Tree Carol' sequence (see page 32) was noted by Cecil Sharp from Charles Smith, aged 49, of Coates in 1909. Laurie Lee tells in *Cider with Rosie* how he and his classmates went round and sang, 'pure, very clear, and breathless' the same carol. They learned it at school, he informed Gwilym Davies. They were probably therefore singing one of the two versions published in *The Oxford Book of Carols* in 1928, which gives an extra verse:

He neither shall be christened in white wine nor in red

But with the fair spring water with which we were christenèd.

The Bitter Willow

It hap-pened to be on one lord's hol-i-day, When a voice from hea-ven called our sweet Christ to his dear mo-ther, Might I play at ball?

'A[t] ball, a[t] ball, dear son', she cried
'It is time that you'd been gone;
And don't let me hear of none of your ill doings
Tonight when you comes home.'

Away, away, run our sweet Christ,
And away and away run he
Until he come to a free dwelled house [yonder town]
And he met three jollian [young lords'] sons.

'Good evening, you three jollian sons;
Your souls to be saved, I pray;
And which of you three jollian sons
Will play a[t] ball with me?'

'We are lords' and ladies' sons,
Borned in the bowers of hall [a bower or hall],
But you are nothing but a poor mother's child,
Born in the auction style [an ox's stall].'

'If you are lords' and ladies' sons
Born in your bowers of hall,
I'll make you repent the very next hour:
I'm an angel above you all.'

Christ built the bridge with the beams of the sun
And across the sea went he;
And these three Jews they followed after him,
And they all got drownded three.

[The it's up the hill and down the hill
These young lords' mothers run:]
'Oh, Mary mild, call in your child;
He now just drowndèd three
[For ours he has drownèd each one].'

Mary took hold of our sweet Christ,
She laid him across her knee;
And with that handful of willow twigs
She give him lashes three.

'Oh, the willow, the bitter willow
It caused my back to smart
But the willow it shall be on the very next [first] tree
It shall die and perish to his heart.

'The Bitter Withy' as it is more usually entitled, is of considerable antiquity, although the first full text was published only in 1905. It consists of incidents from the apocryphal gospels cast into an English setting and given clear social significance. Cecil Sharp noted a version from John Hands of Snowshill in 1909 and the carol was still widely sung at that time. The Gloucestershire poet, F.W. Harvey, recalls in his book *Comrades in Captivity* (1920), how he and other British prisoners-of-war sang the 'quaint little carol' in Germany during the First World War. Our version was recorded at Gloucester in 1966 by Peter Shepheard from the gypsy singer, Lementina ('Lemmie') Brazil, then in her 80s, and from her married sister, Alice Webb. Our version is a collation of the two renderings. It characterises the lords' sons as Jews, but not Jesus himself.

The High-Low Well (Holy Well)

(variation)

As it fell out on a high ho-li-day, As it fell out so high, Sweet
Je-sus, he asked of his own mo-ther dear If he should go out and play.

'To play, to play, dear child', she did say,
'It's time that you were gone,
And don't let me hear of complaint upon you
At night when you come home.'

'Dear mother, I have been to a merry little town
As far as the high-low well,
And there I did see some of the finest children then
That ever any tongue could tell.

'I asked them children, could I play along with them
And they say, "Yes, quite well;
But you are nothing else but a mild Mary's child
Born down in an oxen stall."

Sweet Jesus he turnèd himself short round
Neither to laugh nor to smile;
And the water did fall from sweet Jesus' eyes
Like the water from the sky.

'If you are nothing else but a mild Mary's child
Born down in an ox-film [oxen] stall,
You shall be the king and the crowned of heaven.
And a ruler above us all.'

'Sweet Jesus, go down to the yonder town,
As far as the holy well,
And take away those sinful souls,
And dip them deep in hell'.

'Nay, nay,' sweet Jesus mildly said,
'Nay, nay, that must not be,
For there are too many sinful souls
Crying out for the help of me'.

In 'The Bitter Willow' (see page 36), Mary punishes Jesus for revenging himself on the lords' sons who have spurned him. In 'The High-Low Well' it is she who urges retaliation, and Jesus who declines.

The carol is rare in oral tradition, but a version was noted in 1994 by Gwilym Davies and Paul Burgess from Wisdom ('Wiggie') Smith (aged 69), a gypsy singer living near Tewkesbury. 'The High-Low Well', usually known as 'The Holy Well', was taught to him by his grandfather, and he remembers earning a few pence as a child by singing the carol in a Cotswold pub. The tune given here is Mr Smith's, but his words were incomplete, and additions have been made from other versions. Another tune, allied to a completely different set of words, is given in *Songs of Praise*, no.378.

Divers and Lazarus

As it fell out up - on a day rich Di - vers made a feast. And
he in - vi - ted all his friends and gen - try of the best. Then
Laz - a - rus laid him down and down, and down at Di - vers' door; 'Some
meat, some drink, bro - ther Di - vers, to be - stow up - on the poor.'

'Thou art none of my brothers, Lazarus, lies begging at my door
No meat no drink will I give thee, nor bestow upon the poor.'
Then Lazarus laid him down and down, and down at Divers' gate.
'Some meat, some drink, brother Divers, for Jesus Christ, his sake.'

'Thou art none of my brothers, Lazarus, that lies begging at my gate,
No meat nor drink will I give thee for Jesus Christ, his sake.'
Then Divers sent out his merry men to whip poor Lazarus away;
They had no power to strike a stroke, but flung their whips away.

['Thou art none of my brothers Lazarus, lies begging at my wall;
No meat nor drink will I give thee, but with hunger starve you shall'.]
Then Divers sent two hungry dogs, to bite him as he lay;
They had no power to bite at all, but licked his sores away.

As it fell out upon one day, poor Lazarus sickened and died.
There came two angels out of heaven, his soul therein to guide.
'Rise up, rise up, brother Lazarus, and come along with me,
For there's a place prepared in heaven, to sit on an angel's knee.'

As it fell out upon a day, rich Divers sickened and died.
There came two angels [serpents] out of hell, his soul therein to guide.
'Rise up, rise up, brother Divers, and come along with me,
For there's a place prepared in hell, from which thou canst not flee.'

Then Divers lifted up his eyes and saw poor Lazarus blest:
'Give me one drop of water to quench my flaming thirst.'
If I had as many years to live as there are blades of grass,
[Then there would be an end, but now hell's pains will ne'er be past.

Oh was I now but alive again the space of half an hour]
Then I would find my place secure and the devil should have no power.

The stern lesson presented here derives from the parable of rich Dives and poor Lazarus in *Luke*, chapter 16. The first printed mention of the ballad dates from 1557-8. Our version was recorded in 1954 from Emily Bishop (1879-1961) of Bromsberrow Heath by Russell Wortley. The tune has been transcribed by Pat Palmer. The singer's memory of the words was a little hazy in the final verses, as can be heard on a performance on the cassette, *The Bitter Withy* (see Discography). The first six verses of Emily Bishop's version are very similar to those of a text from Dumbleton noted in 1909.

Christmas is now drawing near at hand

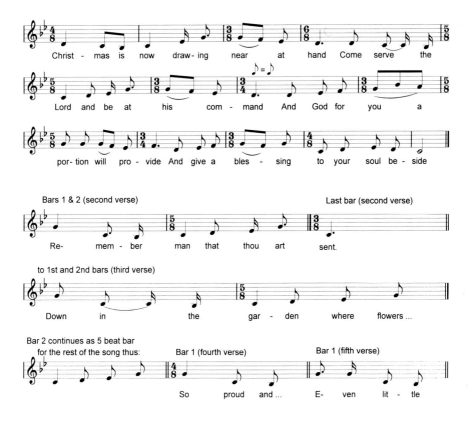

Remember, man, that thou art made of clay
And in this world thou hast not long to stay.
This wicked world will never be content
With all the blessed gifts that God has sent.

Down in the garden where flowers grow in rank
Down on your bended knees and give the Lord thanks;
Down on your knees and pray both night and day
Leave off your sins and live upright and pray.

So proud and lofty is some sort of sin
Which many take delight and pleasure in.
Such conversation God does not dislike
And yet he shakes his sword before he strikes.

So proud and lofty do some people go,
Dressing themselves like players in a show;
They patch and paint and dress with idle stuff,
As if God had not made them fine enough.

Even little children learn to curse and swear
And can't rehearse one word of godly prayer.
Oh teach them better, oh teach them to rely
On Christ, the sinner's friend, who reigns on high.

Instead of joyous expectation, the approach of Christmas here calls forth stern warnings on morality and mortality. The words of this carol, once well known in the Midlands and West of England, seem to derive from a street ballad issued early in the nineteenth century by several London printers. Our version, with its splendid Dorian tune, was recorded in 1954 by Russell Wortley from Emily Bishop (see note to 'On Christmas Night'). The tune has been transcribed by Pat Palmer. A recording made two years earlier by Peter Kennedy appears on the cassette, *Bitter Withy: Early English Folk Carols* (see Discography). This includes verse 4, which is omitted on the later recording.

The Holly and the Ivy

Chorus

The rising of the sun, the running of the deer;
The playing of the merry organ, sweet singing in the choir.

The holly bears a blossom as white as the lily flower,
And Mary bore sweet Jesus Christ to be our sweet saviour.

The holly bears a berry as red as any blood,
And Mary bore sweet Jesus Christ to do poor sinners good.

The holly bears a prickle as sharp as any thorn,
And Mary bore sweet Jesus Christ on Christmas Day in the morn.

The holly bears a bark as bitter as any gall,
And Mary bore sweet Jesus Christ for to redeem us all.

As it happens, the version of this carol now universally known comes from Gloucestershire, for it was noted (substantially) by Cecil Sharp in 1909 from Mrs. Mary A. Clayton (aged 64) of Chipping Campden, and later widely circulated in *The Oxford Book of Carols*. The Hill family of Bromsberrow Heath, recorded in 1980 by Gwilym Davies and Mike Yates, preferred what they called 'the old tune', which is what we give here. A version from only a dozen miles away, at Bromsash near Ross-on-Wye in Herefordshire, can be heard on the cassette, *The Bitter Withy* (see Discography).

A Village Choir, by Thomas Webster
Painted in Bow Brickhill Church, and shown at the R.A. in 1847
Victoria and Albert Museum

The Lily-white Boys

V1
O, I'll sing you one, O. What is your one, O? When the one is left a-lone he ev-er-more shall be so.

V2
O, I'll sing you two, O. What is your two, O? Two, two the li-ly white boys, clo-thèd all in green, O. When the one is left a-lone, he e-ver more shall be so.

V3
O, I'll sing you three O. What is your three, O? Three, three, the riv - o. Two, two, the li-ly white boys.

V4
O, I'll sing you four, O. What is your four, O? Four for the gos-pel prea-chers, three, three, the riv-o.

The song continues, adding a line each verse, until:

O, I'll sing you twelve, O. What is your twelve, O? Twelve for the twelve a-pos-tles,

'leven for the 'leven who went to heaven, Ten for the ten com-man-der's men,

Nine for the nine bright shi-ners, Eight for the Gab-riel stran-gers,

Seven for the seven stars in the sky, Six for the six proud wal-kers,

Five for the sym-bols in my path, Four for the gos-pel prea-chers,

Three, three, the riv - o. Two, two, the li-ly white boys, clo-thèd all in

green, O. When the one is left a-lone he ev-er more shall be so.

46

O, I'll sing you two, O.
What is your two, O?
Two, two, the lily-white boys
Clothèd all in green, O.
When the one is left alone
He evermore shall be so

And so on, with

Three, three the rivo

Four... the gospel preachers

Five... the symbols in my [path]

Six... six proud walkers

Seven...seven stars in the sky

Eight..Gabriel strangers

Nine...nine bright shiners

Ten..the ten commander's men

Eleven ...[the eleven that went to heaven]

Twelve.. twelve for the twelve apostles

Last verse

O, I'll sing you twelve, O.
What is your twelve, O?
Twelve for the twelve apostles,
Eleven for the eleven that went to heaven,
Ten for the ten commander's men,
Nine, the nine bright shiners,
Eight, the Gabriel strangers,
Seven for the seven stars in the sky,
Six for the six proud walkers,
Five for the symbols in my path,
Four for the gospel preachers,
Three, three, the rivo,
Two, two, the lily-white boys
Clothèd all in green, O.
When the one is left alone
He evermore shall be so.

Under the alternative title of 'Green Grow the Rushes, O', this is perhaps the best known English traditional song. It was sung in Cornwall both by chapel congregations and by carol singers at Christmas. In Norfolk it was a favourite at harvest home celebrations. Eton schoolboys enjoyed it, and Sir Arthur Sullivan introduced it into *The Yeomen of the Guard*. Versions have been reported in Breton, Flemish, Hebrew, German, Greek and medieval Latin ('Unus est Deus'). John Moore wrote in *Portrait of Elmbury* (1945) that Gloucestershire villagers sang it 'exquisitely, with a sort of reverential air, as if they knew it was strong magic, which indeed it is'.

Several versions have been found in Gloucestershire, of which the earliest (given here) was recorded in 1908 on a phonograph cylinder by the composer, Percy Grainger, from Mr George Lane (aged 83) of Alstone, who was in the workhouse at Winchcombe at the time. The words sung by John Bradley (aged 71) at Coates to Cecil Sharp in 1912 were very different:

I will sing the twelve, O.
What is your twelve, O?
Twelve are the twelve apostle ships,
Eleven are the eleven bencher ships,
And ten the ten commandments;
Nine the nine bright shiners,
Eight the gibble rangers,
Seven the seven stars in the sky,
And six the six proud walkers,
Five are the symbols in my bosom,
Four the gospel preachers;
Three, three. the riders,
Two and two the lily-white boys,
Clothèd all in green, O;
When the one is left alone
It ever more shall be.

A version which Richard Chidlaw of Dursley learned in 1975 from Mr Cameron Riley Johnson (aged 90) of Yorkley Slade, near Lydney, can be heard on the cassette, *All Brought up on Cider* (see Discography).

Great efforts have been made to explain the song. Perhaps the most convincing theory is that it was a mnemonic for the kabbalistic doctrine of the ten stages between heaven and earth, with the twelve verses of many versions representing a Christian overlay. Whatever the truth, 'I'll sing you one, O' continues to fascinate.

There were two ships

A) Bisley

There were two ships came sail - ing in, There were two ships came
sail - ing in, There were two ships came sail - ing in, Christ- mas Day all in the mor- ning.

B) Brazil

As I walked by the riv - er - side, Riv - er - side, riv - er - side,
I went by the riv - er - side, A Chris- e - mas Day in the mor - ning.

A.

Who do you think were in those two ships? (3)
Christmas Day all in the morning.

Christ was there and his mother too, (3)
Christmas Day all in the morning.

B.

I slipped down the 'oller plank,
'oller plank, 'oller plank,
I slipped down the 'oller plank,
A Chrisemas Day in the morning.

We saw two ships come sailin' by,
Sailin' by, sailin' by,
We saw two ships come sailin' by,
A Chrisemas Day in the morning.

Who do you think was in the ship,
In the ship, in the ship,
Who do you think was in the ship?
Young Joseph and young Mary.

Joseph whistles and Mary sings,
All the bells in heaven rings;
All the bells in heaven rings,
A Chrisemas Day in the morning.

Despite its 'two ships', version A. of the carol (which dates back to the seventeenth century) is better known as 'I saw three ships' or 'As I sat on a sunny bank'. It was learned at Bisley before the First World War by a girl who later moved to Birdlip. Instead of the usual tune, she sang the Gloucestershire favourite, 'George Ridler's Oven' - as did in 1882 Charles Poole of Wotton-under-Edge, whose singing was remembered by Constance, the wife of Cecil Sharp. 'Two Ships' comes from *Birdlip and Brimsfield. The Story of Two Villages, 1850-1957*, edited by R.F. Butler (1959). Version B. was recorded by Peter Shepheard at Gloucester from the gypsy singer, Lemmie Brazil, in 1967.

The Lambskin Carol

Said Ma - ry to Jo - seph, 'I'm cold to my skin. Would that
I had a blan - ket to wrap the babe in, There's nought but a
man - ger for my ba - by's bed, And a pill - ow of straw for to
crad - le his head. To crad - le his head, to crad - le his
head, And a pill - ow of straw for to crad - le his head.'
flee - cy lamb - skin, A flee - cy lamb - skin, To wrap the babe
in, My gift to the ba - by is a flee - cy lamb - skin.

Three wise men came from countries afar;
They followed the light of a beautiful star.
They brought to the infant gifts costly and rare
That they laid at his feet in the stable so bare.

A shepherd came, both humble and poor.
He fell on his knees when the saviour he saw:
'I must give him a gift, a token of love,
For he's fair as an angel from heaven above.'

Said the shepherd to Mary, 'The night it is cold.
You can't wrap a baby in silver or gold.
My gift it is small, it cost not a pin.
My gift to the baby is a fleecy lambskin.

A fleecy lambskin, to wrap the babe in,
My gift to the baby is a fleecy lambskin.'

Maddy Taylor of Cheltenham in a carol written in 1990 treats an ancient theme with freshness and skill. A recording is available on the cassette by Ron Taylor and Geoff Gillett, *Fair Length and Share* (see Discography).

The Christmas Lament

The sage and the red rose climbed over his head.
The nutmeg and the heartsease in the doorway were spread.
The hemlock and the bittersweet that grows up so high,
They bowed themselves harmless, when Christ came to die.

The magpie and the old crow sang sweet by his head,
The twinks and the larks for his coverlet were spread,
The grey quist and the white dove flew down from on high,
As Christ came from heaven when he came to die.

But I sit here sighing, this clear Christmas day
The birds' song and the flowers' scent have faded away.
The world is a cruel place, all grasping and gain,
And 'twill be till peace comes, and Christ comes to reign.

Written by Richard Chidlaw of Dursley in 1975. Twinks are chaffinches and quists are wood pigeons.

Brockweir Wassail

A wis-sel, a was-s'l a-bout our town, The cup it is black and the ale it is brown; The cup it is made of the mul-ber-ry tree, So here, my good fel-low, we'll drink un-to thee.

(a)

Var. (a)
in vv. 2-4

Here's to the quick and to the white horn.
Pray God send the master a good crop of corn,
Both wheat, rye and barley and all sorts of grain,
So here, good fellow, we'll drink to thee again.

If your missus or master they be not at home,
For if they be abroad, God send them safe home;
For if they be at home, let them live at their ease,
So fetch out the white loaf and the whole cheese.

Come all you pretty maidens that reel on your pins,
Pray open the door and let the wass'lers in;
For if you be maidens or if you be none,
Pray don't let the wass'lers stay on the cold stones.

Repeat last two lines

Learnt by Charley Williams in Brockweir in about 1917 and noted by Bob Patten and Andrew Taylor in November 1977; used with permission. Tune transcribed by Pat Palmer. A group of 10 or 20 singers would travel around on 5 and 6 January 'because the people expected us then'. It seems that the custom was kept up until sometime between the First and Second World Wars, both in Brockweir and in nearby St Briavels. See also 'The Waysailing Bowl' (page 56).

The Waysailing Bowl

A) Arlingham

Way - sail, way - sail all o - ver the town, Our toast it is white and our ale it is brown; Our bowl it is made of the sy - ca - more tree; To me way - sail - ing bowl I'll drink un - to thee. Way - sail, way- sail, to me jol - ly way - sail, And joy shall go with our jol - ly way - sail.

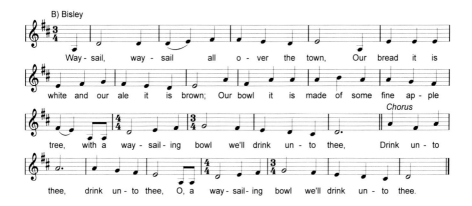

B) Bisley

Way - sail, way - sail all o - ver the town, Our bread it is white and our ale it is brown; Our bowl it is made of some fine ap - ple tree, with a way - sail - ing bowl we'll drink un - to thee, Drink un - to thee, drink un - to thee, O, a way - sail - ing bowl we'll drink un - to thee.

A. from Arlingham

Come butler, come butler, a bowl of your best,
I hope that in heaven your soul it may rest;
But if butler don't bring us a bowl of his small,
Down will go butler, bowl and all.

There was an old woman, she had but one cow,
And how to maintain it she did not know how,
But she built up a barn to keep her cow warm,
And a drop of your cider won't do us no harm.

Here's a health unto Colley and to her right eye,
May God send our master a good Christmas pie,
And a good Christmas pie, that we may all see,
To me waysailing bowl, I'll drink unto thee.

Here's a health unto Colley and to her right leg
God send our master a good fatted pig [pronounced 'peg'];
A good fatted pig, that we may all see,
To me waysailing bowl, I'll drink unto thee.

Here's a health unto Colley and to her right horn,
Pray God send our master a good crop of corn;
A good crop of corn, that we may all see,
To me waysailing bowl, I'll drink unto thee.

Now come all ye maidens, I know there are few [some],
Will not let the waysailers stand on the cold stone,
But lift up the latch and draw back the pin,
And let the waysailers walk merrily in.

B. from Bisley
Here's a health to our master and to his right arm,
May God send our master a good crop of corn;
A good crop of corn, that we may all see,
O, a waysailing bowl, we'll drink unto thee.

Here's a health to our master and to his right leg,
May God send our master a jolly fat pig [pronounced 'peg'];
A jolly fat pig, that we may all see,
O, a waysailing bowl, we'll drink unto thee.

Here's a health to our master and to his right eye,
May God send our master a good Christmas pie;
A good Christmas pie, that we may all see,
O, a waysailing bowl, we'll drink unto thee.

Here's health to our master and to his right hoof,
May God send our master a jolly fat goose;
A jolly fat goose, that we may all see,
O, a waysailing bowl. we'll drink unto thee.

Here's health to our master and to his right ear;
May God send our master a happy New Year;
A happy New Year, that we may all see;
O, a waysailing bowl, we'll drink unto thee.

Come butler, come butler, bring us a bowl of your best;
We hope that in heaven your soul it will rest,
But if you don't bring us a bowl of your small,
Then down will go butler, bowl and all.

Chorus

Bowl and all, *etc.*

There was an old woman, she had but one cow,
And how to maintain it she did not know how;
She built up a fire to keep her cow warm,
And a little of your cider would do us no harm.

Chorus

Do us no harm, *etc.*

We are told that the English troops spent the night before the battle of Hastings in revelry, with cries of 'wassail' and 'drinkhail', or 'good health' and 'the same to you' in modern parlance. There are records from the fourteenth century of the circulation of a wassail bowl with appropriate drinks and good wishes among members of a household on New Year's Eve or Twelfth Night; and by 1600 people were taking bowls round, probably from door to door, offering a drink and expecting money in return. A song (possibly a parody) is mentioned as early as 1550 in John Bale's play, *Kynge Johan*:

Wassail, wassail, out of the milk pail,
Wassail, wassail, as white as any nail,
Wassail, wassail, in snow, frost and hail,
Wassail, wassail, that doth much avail,
Wassail, wassail, that never will fail.

The 'Gloucestershire Wassail' is now nationally known, thanks to the composite version published by Ralph Vaughan Williams in *The Oxford Book of Carols* (1928), but many villages once had their own versions of words and tunes. Wassailing (sometimes called waysailing or walsailing) was widely carried on from Maisemore and Shurdington in the north of Gloucestershire to Little Sodbury and Badminton in the south. As well as a suitably large bowl, which was usually decorated with metal hoops and flowers, wassailers in the south of the county carried a sort of imitation ox known as the Broad. They went from farm to farm and from manor to mansion, anywhere they might expect a welcome and a reward. People gave drink, money, Christmas fare, and in return received good luck for the ensuing year.

Frank Kidson wrote in the 1890s of a Gloucestershire friend who:

'tells me it is, or was until a few years ago, sung by the farm labourers on Christmas Eve, a small band of them going about to the various large farmers carrying a wassail-bowl decorated with ribbons. The bowl was one of those wooden sycamore or maple ones used to hold boiled potatoes on a farm kitchen table. The ribbons were tied to bent withies, which extended over the bowl in a bowed form.'

The friend added that 'if you gave them [the wassailers] liquor enough, they would sing half the night'.

T.H.Packer, writing in 1912 in *The Cheltenham Looker-on*, observed that wassailing in Gloucestershire had 'almost fallen into disuse', though he excepted one area:

'In the neighbourhood of Cranham, Stroud, Painswick and other parts of the Cotswolds the custom was strictly observed, and we are informed that as recently as Boxing Day, 1910, the wassail bowl, prettily decorated with coloured ribbons, fruit, and evergreens, was carried round the parishes of Witcombe and Bentham. According to custom the houses of the leading residents and farmers were visited and this ancient folk-song rendered. ...It is needless to say that this musical offer to pledge the health of the 'measter' and his good lady usually met with a ready response, and, as a further consequence, doubtless the visit of the jocund wassailers was rendered all the pleasanter by their host's financial contribution to the wassail bowl.'

The custom survived in some places, notably Arlingham, Shurdington, Tetbury and Woodchester until the Second World War. The song continued to be sung in village pubs until the 1980s and can still be heard at family gatherings.

Version A., sung by Lem Hayward (1901-1992) of Arlingham, was recorded by Gwilym Davies in January 1977. The custom was kept up until the Second World War in Arlingham, where at about 8 pm on New Year's Eve, a party some twenty strong would set off from Arlingham and call at Framilode, Saul, and Frampton Court. They carried a six-foot bough decorated with tinsel and cards, and collected money in a tin. Lem Hayward's song can be heard on The Horkey Load, vol. 2.

Version B., save for verse 5, was recorded at Bisley by Gwilym and Carol Davies in January 1977 from Madge Stevens, who can be heard on the cassette, *All Brought up on Cider* (see Discography). Until the 1980s, the Stevens family used to sing the song every Christmas in the Stirrup Cup public house at Bisley. Verse 5 has been added from a substantially similar version noted in the 1930s from H.W.Dean of Bisley by James M. Carpenter, who observed that the wassailers used a big washing up bowl trimmed with ribbons, holly, mistletoe, apples and oranges. Another of Carpenter's versions, this time from George Herbert of Avening, can be found in Roy Palmer's book, *The Folklore of Gloucestershire* (1994).

Waisail Bowl from Hillesley, near Wotton-under-Edge
Photo: courtesy of Richard Chidlow

Here we come a-wandering

Here we come a-wand'-ring through the fields so green, And here we come a-wand-er-ing, so faith-ful to be seen. We are not dai-ly beg-gars that beg from door to door, But we are neigh-bours' chil-dren that you have seen be-fore.

Come out the butler of this house, put on your diamond ring,
And bring us out a glass of beer, the better we shall sing;
And bring us out a table and spread it with a cloth,
And bring us out a lump of beef and some of your Christmas love [loaf].

Come all you lucky gentlemen

I ain't come here not to beg and not to borrow,

I have come here just to drive away my sorrow.

A bit of your good cake and a drop of your strong beer,

An' I hope you merry Chris-e-mas an' a happy New Year, New Year,
An' I hope you merry Chris-e-mas an' a happy New Year.

These are fragments of wassail songs. In spite of its reference to children, 'Here we come a-wandering'(page 61) was sung by adults. Richard Chidlaw (who also transcribed the tune) learned it in 1972 from Archie Gardener of Nailsworth (formerly of Avening), and passed it on to Gwilym Davies. Archie and his companions used to sing these two verses before striking up their version of 'The Waysailing Bowl'. 'Come all you lucky gentlemen' is a collation of versions recorded in 1968 at Gloucester by Peter Shepheard from the gypsy singer Lemmie Brazil, and in 1995 by Gwilym Davies from Danny Brazil (aged 85), Lemmie's brother. Tune transcriptions by Shepheard and Davies.

The cock flew up in the yew tree

A.

The cock fled up in the yew tree; the hen came chit- ter- ling by. I

wish you mer- ry Chris- e - mas and ev- 'ry day a pie; A pie, a pudd - 'ney

pep - per- corn, the fat - test pig that ev- er was born, Come o - pen the door and

let the New Year come in. God bless this la - dy of this house, be-

sides the mas- ter, too. Please to leave me a lit- tle piece for sing - ing it so well.

B.

1. The cock fled up in the yew tree, the hen came flut- ter- ing by. I

wish you a mer- ry Christ - mas And a big fat pig in the sty. 2. The

roads are ver - y dirt - y, My shoes are ver - y clean [thin]; I've

got a lit - tle pock - et to put a pen - ny in. 3. If you

hav- en't got a pen - ny, A ha' - p'ny will do. If you

hav- en't got a ha' - p'ny God bless you.

Spoken

And I wish you a mer - ry Christ - mas

64

Variations of this short piece were quite common. A. was noted from the gypsy singer, Wiggie Smith, in Cheltenham by Gwilym Davies and Paul Burgess in August 1994. The tune has been transcribed by Carol Davies. Mr Smith said that it was traditional in his family to go around singing it from caravan to caravan at the New Year. B. was recorded by Roy and Pat Palmer from Stan and Gwen Partridge of Cinderford in July 1994. As children the Partridges concluded each door to door performance of carols with this little *quête* song. Pat Palmer transcribed the tune.

Sherborne Mummers' Song

(Tune 1) for 1st and last verse

To me high ding ding, me high ding ding, me high ding ding do der - ry; We all come here this Christ - mas time, we all come here to get me - rry.

(Tune 2)

Good mas - ter and mis - tress, both sit by the fire, Put your hand in your po- cket, we pray and de - sire, Put your hand in your po - cket and pull out your

Chorus

purse, For a lit - tle of some - thing will do us no hurt, Sing fa the ro ra- ddie, Sing fa the ro ra- ddie, Sing fa the ro ra - ddie ay aye.

Go down in your cellar and see what you find,
Your barrel's not empty, if you will be kind;
If you will be kind with a glass of good beer,
We won't call upon you until the next year.

If you want any matches, come buy them off me;
They are the best matches that ever you did see;
For lighting the candle and starting the fire,
They are the best matches that you can desire.

Here we stand, all [lined] in a row,
Such [very] fine fellows as ever you saw.
Rags nor money we'll never deny,
But a glass of good beer, for we be all very dry.

To me high ding ding, me high ding ding,
Me high ding ding do derry;
We all come here this Christmas time,
We all come here to get merry.

Many of the Cotswold mummers' plays end with a song, sometimes relevant, sometimes not. This came at the end of the Sherborne play and was recorded on a phonograph cylinder by the American, James Carpenter, from William Bunting in the early 1930s. Mr Bunting in turn had learned the play and the song from Tom Pitts (1855-1940), a morris dancer and pipe and tabor player, in about 1880. The main tune is reminiscent of the Scottish air 'Highland Mary', which was used for morris dancing in many Cotswold villages, including Sherborne. The song also has echoes of the northern pace-egg plays. Tunes transcribed by Carpenter.

We wish you a merry Christmas

Sung by Miss Jessie Howman (aged 72) at Stow-on-the-Wold; recorded by Roy Palmer in August 1966, and published in *Songs of the Midlands* (1972). According to *Notes and Queries concerning Evesham and the Four Shires* (ed. E.A.B. Barnard, 1911), a very similar verse served at Dumbleton for wassailing apple trees, with the addition of:

Bud well, bear well,

God send farewell.

Every sprig and every spray,

A bushel of apples

On New Year's Day.

These words in turn are close to 'Buff Blow' (page 69).

Buff Blow

Buff blow, fare well.
God send you e'er well.
Apples to roast, nuts to crack,
A barrel of cider ready to tap,
On New Year's Day in the morning.
Shoo-ee!

Spoken

The old year's out, the New Year's in,
Please open the door and let us in
On New Year's Day in the morning.
Shoo-ee!

This was sung, or chanted, every New Year's morning by the children of Charlton Kings, once a separate village, but now a part of Cheltenham. The custom, known as 'Buff Blowing' or 'the Boy Visitor' was carried on until the 1960s when children, preferably dark-haired, visited houses in the area in the early morning chanting the rhyme. The verses were learnt by Gwilym and Carol Davies in Charlton Kings in the 1970s from various people, including George Maisey, who can be heard talking about the custom and singing his version of the song on the cassette, *All Brought up on Cider*. The complete song was recorded by the Green Willow Band on the LP, *Cotswold Music* (see Discography).

At Gotherington and Woolstone near Cheltenham and at Upton St Leonards near Gloucester, children went round with a similar rhyme, to be rewarded with apples and cakes:

Blow well and bud well,
God send you fare well.
Every sprig and every spray,
A bushel of apples to be given away
On New Year's Day in the morning.

DISCOGRAPHY & BIBLIOGRAPHY

DISCOGRAPHY

Cassettes

All Brought up on Cider. Gloucestershire songs and customs (Folktracks 60-416, 1987).

The Bitter Withy: Early English Folk Carols (Folktracks 60-504, 1978.)

Carol Barking, PuzzleJug (PJ1, 1993).

Fair Length and Share, Ron Taylor and Geoff Gillett (RED 019, 1996).

The Horkey Load, vol. 2 (Veteran Tapes VT109, 1988).

No, sir, No - Songs and Carols from the West Midlands, (Folktracks 60-129, 1980).

LPs

Cotswold Music, the Green Willow Band (SFA115, 1980).

Songs of Ceremony (Topic 12T197, 1971).

BIBLIOGRAPHY

W.E. Adams, *Memoirs of a Social Atom*, 2 vols (1903)

Fred Archer, *The Distant Scene* (1967)

E.A.B. Barnard (ed.), *Notes and Queries concerning the Four Shires*, 2 vols (1911)

R.F.Butler (ed.), *Birdlip and Brimsfield. The Story of Two Villages*, (1959)

Gwilym Davies, 'I'll give you the Waysailing Bowl, the Gloucestershire Waysailing Bowl', *English Dance and Song*, Christmas 1988.

Gwilym Davies, 'A Gloucestershire New Year Custom', *Folkwrite*, No 6 (1979)

A Choice Collection of Christmas Carols. No. 1, printed and sold by S. Harward, Tewkesbury
      (copy in the British Library at pressmark 11621 c 1)

A Good Christmas Box, ed. M. and J. Raven (Wolverhampton, 1967; orig. Dudley, 1847)

F.W.Harvey *Comrades in Captivity* (1920)

Hugh Keyte and Andrew Parrott (eds), *The New Oxford Book of Carols* (Oxford, 1992)

Frank Kidson, 'Notes on Old Tunes. A Wassail Song, &c.', *Leeds Mercury*, c. 1890 (copy
      in Leeds City Library)

Laurie Lee, *Cider with Rosie* (1959)

The Methodist Hymn Book (1933)

The Oxford Book of Carols, ed. Percy Dearmer, Ralph Vaughan Williams and Martin Shaw (1967; orig. 1928)

T.H.Packer, 'Some Gloucestershire Songs and Some Old Time and Present Day Christmas Customs', *The Cheltenham Looker-on* (21 Dec. 1912)

Roy Palmer, *The Folklore of Gloucestershire* (Tiverton, 1994)

Roy Palmer, Pamela Bishop and Katharine Thomson (eds), *Songs of the Midlands* (East Ardsley, 1972)

Amy Roberson, (arr.), *Three Ancient Christmas Carols*, Ashton-under-Hill (Evesham, nd)

Cecil Sharp, *Cecil Sharp's Collection of English Folk Songs*, ed. Maud Karpeles, 2 vols (1974)

Cecil Sharp, *English Folk Carols* (1911)

Songs of Praise, ed. Percy Dearmer, Ralph Vaughan Williams and Martin Shaw (1958; orig. 1926)

Joshua Sylvester, *A Garland of Christmas Carols, Ancient and Modern* (1861)

J.E.Vaux, *Church Folklore* (1894)

Index of Titles and First Lines

Index of place names

Little Sodbury 59
Longney 19
Lydney 49

Maisemore 59
Morton Valence 19

Nailsworth 63Newent 30

Old Sodbury 22

Saul 60
Sherborne 67
Shurdington 22, 59
Snowshill 37
St Briavels 55
Staunton 25
Stow-on-the-Wold 68

Tewkesbury 8, 15, 25, 39, 73

Upton St Leonards 70

Winchcombe 48
Woolstone 70
Wotton-under-Edge 51, 61

Yorkley Slade 49